Manual of Dermatologic Therapeutics

With Essentials of Diagnosis